Edition Schott

Cello Library · Cello-Bibliothek

Ludwig van Beethoven

1770 – 1827

Sonatina

for Violoncello and Piano
für Violoncello und Klavier

C minor / c-Moll / Ut mineur

WoO 43a

Arranged from the original version for Mandolin and Piano by /
Nach dem Original für Mandoline und Klavier bearbeitet von
Julius Berger

CB 236
ISMN 979-0-001-17937-9

www.schott-music.com

Mainz · London · Berlin · Madrid · New York · Paris · Prague · Tokyo · Toronto
© 2012 SCHOTT MUSIC GmbH & Co. KG, Mainz · Printed in Germany

Vorwort

Im Jahr 1796, dem Erscheinungsjahr des Streichtrios op. 3, reiste Beethoven nach Prag. Dort traf er die Gräfin Josephine von Clary-Aldringen (1777–1828, ab 1797 verheiratete Gräfin Clamm-Gallas), die Mandoline spielte. Für sie schrieb er einige Werke für Mandoline und Klavier, von denen vier erhalten sind, die ich für Violoncello und Klavier übertragen habe. Beethoven schrieb für eine Mandoline der Stimmung g-d-a-e. Dies macht die Transkription für Violoncello unproblematisch.

1931 erschien in einer Bearbeitung durch den Cellisten J. Stutschewsky die Sonatine WoO 43a für Violoncello, allerdings in d-Moll, nicht in der Originaltonart c-Moll. Bereits Steven Isserlis hat die Variationen WoO 44b im Jahr 1990 mit leichten Korrekturen der Solostimme herausgegeben.
Ich habe mich für eine Übertragung in den Originaltonarten und möglichst nahe am Original entschieden. Das Tasteninstrument bezeichnet Beethoven hier mit „Cembalo", meint aber das damals gebräuchliche Hammerklavier. Darauf deuten auch die dynamischen Vorschriften in WoO 43b hin.

Diese vier eleganten Werke Beethovens sind kleine, leuchtende Juwelen. Auf die einsätzige, mit „Adagio" überschriebene Sonatina WoO 43a in der tragischen Tonart c-Moll mit einem lichten C-Dur-Teil in der Mitte folgt ein herrliches „Adagio ma non troppo" WoO 43b von religiöser Tiefe.

Julius Berger

Preface

In 1796, the year of publication of his String Trio Op. 3, Beethoven travelled to Prague. There he met Countess Josephine von Clary-Aldringen (1777–1828, Countess Clamm-Gallas after her marriage in 1797), who played the mandolin. For her he wrote a few works for mandolin and piano, of which four have survived: I have transcribed these for cello and piano. Beethoven wrote for a mandolin with strings tuned to G-D-A-E, which makes transcription for the cello quite straightforward.

In 1931 the Sonatina WoO 43a was published in an arrangement for the cello by the cellist J. Stuchevsky – though in D minor, not the original key of C minor. Steven Isserlis also edited the Variations WoO 44b for publication in 1990, with some slight changes to the solo part. I decided to keep my transcription as close as possible to the original, using the original keys. Beethoven referred to the keyboard instrument in question as 'Cembalo' [harpsichord] but presumably meant the fortepiano then in general use – this is also suggested by dynamic markings in WoO 43b.

These four elegant pieces by Beethoven are bright little gems. The one-movement Sonatina WoO 43a with 'Adagio' written at the top is in the tragic key of C minor with a bright C major section in the middle; it is followed by a wonderful 'Adagio ma non troppo' WoO 43b of religious profundity.

Julius Berger
Translation Julia Rushworth

Violoncello

Fingersatz und Strichbezeichnung von
Fingering and bowing by
Julius Berger

Sonatine
WoO 43a (179b)

Ludwig van Beethoven
1770–1827

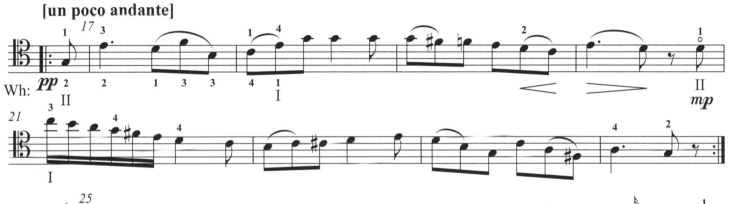

[un poco andante]

D. C. al ⊕–⊕

Fine

© 2012 Schott Music GmbH & Co. KG, Mainz · Printed in Germany   54 528

Sonatine
WoO 43a (179b)

Ludwig van Beethoven
1770–1827

54 528

6

[un poco andante]

D. C. al ⊕–⊕

Fine

Schott Music, Mainz 54 528